The Walrus and the Carpenter
and other poems

by Lewis Carroll

pictures by Gerald Rose

E. P. Dutton & Co., Inc.   New York

This edition first published in the U.S.A. 1969. Copyright © 1968 by Faber and Faber and published under the title *Jabberwocky and Other Poems.* Printed in Great Britain. All rights reserved. Library of Congress Catalog Card Number: 69–10834

THE WALRUS AND THE CARPENTER

The sun was shining on the sea,
Shining with all his might:
He did his very best to make
The billows smooth and bright—
And this was odd, because it was
The middle of the night.

The moon was shining sulkily,
Because she thought the sun
Had got no business to be there
After the day was done—
"It's very rude of him," she said,
"To come and spoil the fun!"

The sea was wet as wet could be,
　The sands were dry as dry.
You could not see a cloud because
　No cloud was in the sky:
No birds were flying overhead—
　There were no birds to fly.

The Walrus and the Carpenter
　Were walking close at hand:
They wept like anything to see
　Such quantities of sand:
"If this were only cleared away,"
　They said, "it *would* be grand!"

"If seven maids with seven mops
　　Swept it for half a year,
Do you suppose," the Walrus said,
　　"That they could get it clear?"
"I doubt it," said the Carpenter,
　　And shed a bitter tear.

"O Oysters, come and walk with us!"
　　The Walrus did beseech.
"A pleasant walk, a pleasant talk,
　　Along the briny beach:
We cannot do with more than four,
　　To give a hand to each."

The eldest Oyster looked at him,
　　But never a word he said:
The eldest Oyster winked his eye,
　　And shook his heavy head—
Meaning to say he did not choose
　　To leave the oyster-bed.

But four young Oysters hurried up,
   All eager for the treat:
Their coats were brushed, their faces washed,
   Their shoes were clean and neat—
And this was odd, because, you know,
   They hadn't any feet.

Four other Oysters followed them,
   And yet another four;
And thick and fast they came at last,
   And more, and more, and more—
All hopping through the frothy waves,
   And scrambling to the shore.

The Walrus and the Carpenter
   Walked on a mile or so,
And then they rested on a rock
   Conveniently low:
And all the little Oysters stood
   And waited in a row.

"The time has come," the Walrus said,
   "To talk of many things:
Of shoes—and ships—and sealing-wax—
   Of cabbages—and kings—
And why the sea is boiling hot—
   And whether pigs have wings."

"But wait a bit," the Oysters cried,
    "Before we have our chat;
For some of us are out of breath,
    And all of us are fat!"
"No hurry!" said the Carpenter.
    They thanked him much for that.

"A loaf of bread," the Walrus said,
    "Is what we chiefly need:
Pepper and vinegar besides
    Are very good indeed—
Now, if you're ready, Oysters dear,
    We can begin to feed."

"But not on us!" the Oysters cried,
    Turning a little blue.
"After such kindness, that would be
    A dismal thing to do!"
"The night is fine," the Walrus said.
    "Do you admire the view?"

"It was so kind of you to come!
    And you are very nice!"
The Carpenter said nothing but
    "Cut us another slice.
I wish you were not quite so deaf—
    I've had to ask you twice!"

"It seems a shame," the Walrus said,
    "To play them such a trick.
After we've brought them out so far,
    And made them trot so quick!"
The Carpenter said nothing but
    "The butter's spread too thick!"

"I weep for you," the Walrus said:
    "I deeply sympathize."
With sobs and tears he sorted out
    Those of the largest size,
Holding his pocket-handkerchief
    Before his streaming eyes.

"O Oysters," said the Carpenter,
    "You've had a pleasant run!
Shall we be trotting home again?"
    But answer came there none—
And this was scarcely odd, because
    They'd eaten every one.

"YOU ARE OLD, FATHER WILLIAM"

"You are old, Father William," the young man said,
  "And your hair has become very white;
And yet you incessantly stand on your head—
  Do you think, at your age, it is right?"

"In my youth," Father William replied to his son,
  "I feared it might injure the brain;
But, now that I'm perfectly sure I have none,
  Why, I do it again and again."

"You are old," said the youth, "as I mentioned before,
  And have grown most uncommonly fat;
Yet you turned a back-somersault in at the door—
  Pray, what is the reason of that?"

"In my youth," said the sage, as he shook his grey locks,
  "I kept all my limbs very supple
By the use of this ointment—one shilling the box—
  Allow me to sell you a couple?"

"You are old," said the youth, "and your jaws are too weak
  For anything tougher than suet;
Yet you finished the goose, with the bones and the beak—
  Pray, how did you manage to do it?"

"In my youth," said his father, "I took to the law,
  And argued each case with my wife;
And the muscular strength, which it gave to my jaw,
  Has lasted the rest of my life."

"You are old," said the youth, "one would hardly suppose
  That your eye was as steady as ever;
Yet you balanced an eel on the end of your nose—
  What made you so awfully clever?"

"I have answered three questions, and that is enough,"
  Said his father. "Don't give yourself airs!
Do you think I can listen all day to such stuff?
  Be off, or I'll kick you down-stairs!"

THE LOBSTER QUADRILLE

"Will you walk a little faster?" said a whiting to a snail,
"There's a porpoise close behind us, and he's treading on my tail.
See how eagerly the lobsters and the turtles all advance!
They are waiting on the shingle—will you come and join the dance?
  Will you, won't you, will you, won't you, will you join the dance?
  Will you, won't you, will you, won't you, won't you join the dance?"

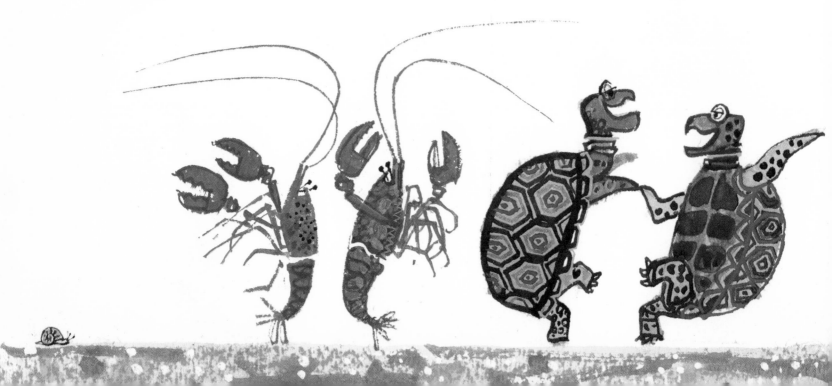

"You can really have no notion how delightful it will be
When they take us up and throw us, with the lobsters, out to sea!"
But the snail replied "Too far, too far!" and gave a look askance—
Said he thanked the whiting kindly, but he would not join the dance.
  Would not, could not, would not, could not, would not join the
    dance.
  Would not, could not, would not, could not, could not join the
    dance.

"What matters it how far we go?" his scaly friend replied,
"There is another shore, you know, upon the other side.
The further off from England the nearer is to France—
Then turn not pale, beloved snail, but come and join the dance.
  Will you, won't you, will you, won't you, will you join the dance?
  Will you, won't you, will you, won't you, won't you join the dance?"

THE MAD GARDENER'S SONG

He thought he saw an Elephant,
   That practised on a fife:
He looked again, and found it was
   A letter from his wife.
"At length I realize," he said,
   "The bitterness of Life!"

He thought he saw a Buffalo
   Upon the chimney-piece:
He looked again, and found it was
   His Sister's Husband's Niece,
"Unless you leave this house," he said,
   "I'll send for the Police!"

He thought he saw a Rattlesnake
   That questioned him in Greek:
He looked again, and found it was
   The Middle of Next Week.
"The one thing I regret," he said,
   "Is that it cannot speak!"

He thought he saw a Banker's Clerk
    Descending from the 'bus:
He looked again, and found it was
    A Hippopotamus.
"If this should stay to dine," he said,
    "There won't be much for us!"

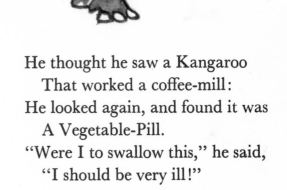

He thought he saw a Kangaroo
    That worked a coffee-mill:
He looked again, and found it was
    A Vegetable-Pill.
"Were I to swallow this," he said,
    "I should be very ill!"

He thought he saw a Coach-and-Four
    That stood beside his bed:
He looked again, and found it was
    A Bear without a Head
"Poor thing," he said, "poor silly thing!
    It's waiting to be fed!"

He thought he saw an Albatross
  That fluttered round the lamp:
He looked again, and found it was
  A Penny-Postage-Stamp.
"You'd best be getting home," he said,
  "The nights are very damp!"

He thought he saw a Garden-Door
  That opened with a key:
He looked again, and found it was
  A Double Rule of Three:
"And all its mystery," he said,
  "Is clear as day to me!"

He thought he saw an Argument
  That proved he was the Pope:
He looked again, and found it was
  A Bar of Mottled Soap.
"A fact so dread," he faintly said,
  "Extinguishes all hope!"

TWEEDLEDUM AND TWEEDLEDEE

Tweedledum and Tweedledee
  Agreed to have a battle;
For Tweedledum said Tweedledee
  Had spoiled his nice new rattle.

Just then flew down a monstrous crow,
  As black as a tar-barrel;
Which frightened both the heroes so,
  They quite forgot their quarrel!

THE LITTLE MAN
THAT HAD A LITTLE GUN

In stature, the Manlet was dwarfish—
    No burly big Blunderbore he:
And he wearily gazed on the crawfish
    His Wifelet had dressed for his tea.
"Now reach me, sweet Atom, my gunlet,
    And hurl the old shoelet for luck:
Let me hie to the bank of the runlet,
    And shoot thee a Duck!"

She has reached him his minikin gunlet:
    She has hurled the old shoelet for luck:
She is busily baking a bunlet,
    To welcome him home with his Duck.
On he speeds, never wasting a wordlet,
    Though thoughtlets cling, closely as wax,
To the spot where the beautiful birdlet
    So quietly quacks.

Where the Lobsterlet lurks, and the Crablet
　　So slowly and sleepily crawls:
Where the Dolphin's at home, and the Dablet
　　Pays long ceremonious calls:
Where the grublet is sought by the Froglet:
　　Where the Frog is pursued by the Duck:
Where the Ducklet is chased by the Doglet—
　　So runs the world's luck!

He has loaded with bullet and powder:
　　His footfall is noiseless as air:
But the Voices grow louder and louder,
　　And bellow, and bluster, and blare.
They bristle before him and after,
　　They flutter above and below,
Shrill shriekings of lubberly laughter,
　　Weird wailings of woe!

They echo without him, within him:
　　They thrill through his whiskers and beard:
Like a teetotum seeming to spin him,
　　With sneers never hitherto sneered.
"Avengement," they cry, "on our Foelet!
　　Let the Manikin weep for our wrongs!
Let us drench him, from toplet to toelet,
　　With Nursery-Songs!

"He shall muse upon 'Hey! Diddle! Diddle!'
   On the Cow that surmounted the Moon:
He shall rave of the Cat and the Fiddle,
   And the Dish that eloped with the Spoon:
And his soul shall be sad for the Spider,
   When Miss Muffet was sipping her whey,
That so tenderly sat down beside her,
      And scared her away!

"The music of Midsummer-madness
   Shall sting him with many a bite,
Till, in rapture of rollicking sadness,
   He shall groan with a gloomy delight:
He shall swathe him, like mists of the morning,
   In platitudes luscious and limp,
Such as deck, with a deathless adorning,
      The Song of the Shrimp!

"When the Ducklet's dark doom is decided,
   We will trundle him home in a trice:
And the banquet, so plainly provided,
   Shall round into rose-buds and rice:
In a blaze of pragmatic invention
   He shall wrestle with Fate, and shall reign:
But he has not a friend fit to mention,
   So hit him again!"

He has shot it, the delicate darling!
   And the Voices have ceased from their strife:
Not a whisper of sneering or snarling,
   As he carries it home to his wife:
Then cheerily champing the bunlet
   His spouse was so skilful to bake,
He hies him once more to the runlet,
   To fetch her the Drake!

SPEAK ROUGHLY
TO YOUR LITTLE BOY

Speak roughly to your little boy,
　　And beat him when he sneezes:
He only does it to annoy,
　　Because he knows it teases.

I speak severely to my boy,
　　I beat him when he sneezes;
For he can thoroughly enjoy
　　The pepper when he pleases!

'TIS THE VOICE OF THE LOBSTER

'Tis the voice of the lobster: I heard him declare,
"You have baked me too brown, I must sugar my hair.
As a duck with its eyelids, so he with his nose
Trims his belt and his buttons, and turns out his toes.
When the sands are all dry, he is gay as a lark,
And will talk in contemptuous tones of the Shark:
But, when the tide rises and sharks are around,
His voice has a timid and tremulous sound.

I passed by his garden, and marked, with one eye,
How the Owl and the Panther were sharing a pie:
The Panther took pie-crust, and gravy, and meat,
While the Owl had the dish as its share of the treat.
When the pie was all finished, the Owl, as a boon,
Was kindly permitted to pocket the spoon:
While the Panther received knife and fork with a growl,
And concluded the banquet by——

A-SITTING ON A GATE

I'll tell thee everything I can:
  There's little to relate.
I saw an aged aged man,
  A-sitting on a gate.
"Who are you, aged man?" I said.
  "And how is it you live?"
And his answer trickled through my head,
  Like water through a sieve.

He said "I look for butterflies
  That sleep among the wheat:
I make them into mutton-pies,
  And sell them in the street.
I sell them unto men," he said,
  "Who sail on stormy seas;
And that's the way I get my bread——
  A trifle, if you please."

But I was thinking of a plan
　　To dye one's whiskers green,
And always use so large a fan
　　That they could not be seen.
So, having no reply to give
　　To what the old man said,
I cried "Come, tell me how you live!"
　　And thumped him on the head.

His accents mild took up the tale:
　　He said "I go my ways,
And when I find a mountain-rill,
　　I set it in a blaze;
And thence they make a stuff they call
　　Rowland's Macassar-Oil—
Yet twopence-halfpenny is all
　　They give me for my toil."

But I was thinking of a way
  To feed oneself on batter,
And so go on from day to day
  Getting a little fatter.
I shook him well from side to side,
  Until his face was blue:
"Come, tell me how you live," I cried,
  "And what it is you do!"

He said "I hunt for haddocks' eyes
  Among the heather bright,
And work them into waistcoat-buttons
  In the silent night.
And these I do not sell for gold
  Or coin of silvery shine,
But for a copper halfpenny,
  And that will purchase nine.

"I sometimes dig for buttered rolls,
    Or set limed twigs for crabs:
I sometimes search the grassy knolls
    For wheels of Hansom-cabs.
And that's the way" (he gave a wink)
    "By which I get my wealth——
And very gladly will I drink
    Your Honour's noble health."

I heard him then, for I had just
    Completed my design
To keep the Menai bridge from rust
    By boiling it in wine.
I thanked him much for telling me
    The way he got his wealth,
But chiefly for his wish that he
    Might drink my noble health.

And now, if e'er by chance I put
  My fingers into glue,
Or madly squeeze a right-hand foot
  Into a left-hand shoe,
Or if I drop upon my toe
  A very heavy weight,
I weep, for it reminds me so
Of that old man I used to know—
Whose look was mild, whose speech was slow,
Whose hair was whiter than the snow,
Whose face was very like a crow,
With eyes, like cinders, all aglow,
Who seemed distracted with his woe,
Who rocked his body to and fro,
And muttered mumblingly and low,
As if his mouth were full of dough,
Who snorted like a buffalo——
That summer evening long ago,
  A-sitting on a gate.

HOW DOTH THE LITTLE CROCODILE

How doth the little crocodile
  Improve his shining tail,
And pour the waters of the Nile
  On every golden scale!

How cheerfully he seems to grin,
  How neatly spreads his claws,
And welcomes little fishes in,
  With gently smiling jaws!

JABBERWOCKY

'Twas brillig, and the slithy toves
   Did gyre and gimble in the wabe:
All mimsy were the borogoves,
   And the mome raths outgrabe.

"Beware the Jabberwock, my son!
   The jaws that bite, the claws that catch!
Beware the Jubjub bird, and shun
   The frumious Bandersnatch!"

He took his vorpal sword in hand:
   Long time the manxome foe he sought—
So rested he by the Tumtum tree,
   And stood awhile in thought.

And, as in uffish thought he stood,
  The Jabberwock, with eyes of flame,
Came whiffling through the tulgey wood,
  And burbled as it came!

One, two! One, two! And through and through
  The vorpal blade went snicker-snack!
He left it dead, and with its head
  He went galumphing back.

"And hast thou slain the Jabberwock?
  Come to my arms, my beamish boy!
O frabjous day! Callooh! Callay!"
  He chortled in his joy.

'Twas brillig, and the slithy toves
  Did gyre and gimble in the wabe:
All mimsy were the borogoves,
  And the mome raths outgrabe.

CONTENTS

727436 ✓✓

Date Due

DISCARDED

DISCARDED

DISCARDED

DATE DUE